# The Prayer Playbook

**A 21-Day Workbook to Begin, Transform, and Improve Your Prayer Life**

## JAZLYN DENISE

To Kisha
Many Blessings

The Prayer Playbook: A 21-Day Workbook to Begin, Transform, and Improve Your Prayer Life

Copyright © 2020 by Jazlyn Denise Turner

Published by Holy Ground Ministries Publishing
Inglewood, California 90302

**Printed in the United States of America**

ISBN 978-1-7346700-0-4 (pbk.)
ISBN 978-1-7346700-1-1 (eBook)

**Visit the author's website at JazlynDenise.com**

Interior Layout and Exterior Design by: Jera Publishing
Edited by: Candice L. Davis
Author Photo by: Gebel Tarik Baucham

# Dedication

*clears throat*
First giving honor to God who is the head of my life, driving force, and true author
of this book. I thank you for wisdom, guidance, and direction.

To my paternal grandparents,
Clifton D. Turner and Frances Murdock Turner, who both passed away before I was
born. May your memories continue to teach me lessons of love.

To my maternal grandparents,
a man of many words, the late Pastor Milton M. Merriweather, and my ever present
Angel, Gloria S. Gammage Merriweather, I thank you for setting the foundation of
God in our family.

To my parents,
the overly organized Clifton E. Turner and my voice of truth Alice M. Turner
Sanders, I thank you for giving me an abundant life full of wisdom, love
and laughter.

To my SONshine,
Jeremy C. Turner Jeter , you changed me forever and more than anything I pray
that I have set an example of what a relationship with God looks like. Your kind,
gentle and caring spirit, are a true reflection of God's love. As you grow and mature,
keep God first and remember Momma always knows best.

To my family, friends and loved ones,
I thank you for your love and support. I could write another book naming you all
individually and expressing my gratitude.

Finally, to my younger self, walk in your purpose,
let the light God placed in you shine bright for all to see.
You are loved favored, anointed, fearfully and wonderfully made.
God chose you for such a time as this.

# Contents

# How to Use This Workbook

Prayer is a very powerful tool used by believers to communicate with God. The purpose of this workbook is to dispel the myth that prayer has to be a prescribed set of words or phrases. Use this 21-day workbook to create an infrastructure for your prayer life and become comfortable with going to God directly and interceding on behalf of others. In order to better communicate with God, you have to make your prayers personal. The prayers you'll find in this workbook should serve as templates or guides for the prayers you develop for yourself.

This 21-day workbook was developed to help you learn: the ACTS method of prayer, the benefits of having a sacred space or prayer closet, the power of praying out loud with confidence, steps to identify a prayer partner, and other tools to develop a closer relationship with God, and clearly hear His voice. As you strengthen your relationship with God, you will begin to have more direction, clarity, insight, and peace in your life.

Simply put, prayer is your time to communicate with God. It is also very important to understand because your relationship with God isn't like anyone else's, how you communicate with Him will not be the same. Everyone has a different prayer journey. Having an open line of communication where you also listen to God is the key factor to a successful prayer life. The Bible tells us in Psalm 34:17 that God hears our cry. When you enter into a relationship with God, He knows your heart, He knows your thoughts, trials, and tribulations. He's just waiting for you to bring them to Him. It's important to have daily communication with God to strengthen your relationship. Although you cannot visibly see God, your relationship and communication with Him are as important as those relationships that are physically tangible.

Think about a marriage in which you don't spend time with or talk to your spouse. How can your relationship grow? How will you get to know your spouse? How will you acknowledge each other's feelings? If you don't communicate, do you really have a healthy, intentional, or fruitful relationship?

It's just as important to spend quality time with God, and make it a habit to talk to Him throughout the day. It can be as simple as saying, "Thank you God for letting me be on time for my meeting" or "God, I need you now!" As you develop a better relationship with God, you will get into a prayer regimen you're comfortable with.

The exercises in this workbook will help you learn to pray more constructively and more consistently. It is important to spend quality time with God and create a routine that works best with your schedule. During this time, it is best practice to begin with praise, worship, and gratitude. The Bible tells us in Psalm 100:1-5 to be glad, sing before the Lord, enter into His presence with praise, and thanksgiving. Listen to and sing worship music, dim the lights, light a candle, get comfortable, and set the tone for your time with God. After your praise and worship, begin praying or writing the thoughts of your heart. Once you've done that, just be quiet and still allowing God to speak to you. Understand this is not a rule book. You should do what feels authentic. Remember you can praise, worship, or pray to God anytime.

To encourage you on your prayer journey, I've created a special video resource to provide you with a model of praying out loud and a deeper explanation of the importance of this essential practice.

www.JazlynDenise.com/theprayerplaybookoffer

# The Playbook

## Introduction

I grew up in the church my maternal grandparents founded in their living room, with six members, in 1952. From these humble beginnings, the power of prayer is evident in the many lives they transformed. I heard my grandfather preach and teach about prayer, week in and week out. Not only did I hear this at church, but I also heard it at home as a PK (Preacher's Kid) because my father was also an ordained minister. As a young girl, I knew I was supposed to pray but didn't know the importance and significance of prayer.

Every night I prayed, "Now I lay me down to sleep, I pray the Lord my soul to keep. If I should die before I wake, I pray the Lord my soul to take. Amen." As an adult reflecting on this commonly recited childhood prayer, I laugh at the brevity and content. The sole purpose of this prayer is to ask the Lord to keep my young, precious soul if I die in my sleep. A little harsh for a child, right? Another daily recited childhood prayer was "God is great. God is good. Let us thank Him for our food. Amen!" This, at least, is a little more heartwarming.

Every night, I saw my mother pray silently, on her knees, at the side of my parents' bed. Although I never knew what she was saying, I knew she was humble and sincere in her prayer. Like many little girls, I did what my mother did and I kneeled at the side of my bed and "prayed." We also prayed together. Every morning before she put her car in reverse, we said in unison, "Thank you, Father, for waking us up this morning. Please let us have a blessed and safe day. Amen." This is something I carried on with my son, with a slight variation. "Thank you, Father, for waking us up this morning. Please let us have a blessed, safe, peaceful, and prosperous day. Amen!"

My first memory of praying a prayer outside of my traditional daily prayers was during the summer of 1995. My mother didn't come home after work, and I overheard my father on the phone telling someone my maternal grandmother had a heat stroke and was in the hospital. At the time, I had no idea what a heat stroke was, but I did know being in the hospital wasn't a good sign. As tears streamed down my face, I pleaded with God, "Please heal my grandmother and let her come home healthy." I could hear my grandfather's voice in my head saying, "God will, but only if you let Him," and in that moment I was willing to "let" God do whatever needed to be done to get my grandmother home. I don't remember what time my mother returned from the hospital or when my grandmother was released, but I do remember rushing to her bedroom the next day after school and giving her as many hugs and kisses as she would allow. I knew then that God not only heard my prayer, but that He saw fit to answer it as well.

My journey as a prayer warrior began at a time when I was yearning to be closer to God. Although I grew up seeing the power of prayer and how it changed things, I didn't know if I was praying correctly, and I was always terrified to pray out loud. I felt as if I didn't have the right words to say or that I would be judged if my prayer wasn't "good enough". I later learned that fear was the enemy's way of keeping me trapped. The Bible tells us, in Proverbs 18:21, "Death and life are in the power of the tongue, and those who love it will eat its fruit." By keeping silent, I was blocking my blessings and hindering what God had for me. I knew I had to be released of this stronghold, so I dug deep in my Bible to find God's thoughts, methods, and purpose for prayer.

In Luke 18:1, Jesus tells a parable to illustrate that it's necessary to always pray and not lose heart. God does not make prayer optional, it's something we are required to do. When the disciples ask Jesus to teach them how to pray, He gave them the ultimate template known as The Lord's Prayer, in Luke 11:2-4 (also found in Matthew 6:9-13). Jesus says, "When you pray, say: Our Father, who is in heaven, hallowed be Your name. Your kingdom come; Your will be done on earth, as it is in heaven. Give us each day our daily bread. And forgive us our sins, for we also forgive everyone who is indebted to us. And lead us not into temptation but deliver us from evil."

Notice that He tells them *when* you pray, not *if* you pray. The word "when" makes this a directive or command. Here is a simple breakdown of this passage:

*Our Father, who is in heaven, hallowed be Your name.*

Jesus acknowledges God, His presence, and the sacredness of His name.

*Your kingdom come; Your will be done on earth, as it is in heaven.*

He then asks that the will of God be done in the same divine order as it is in heaven, since heaven is a place of peace and serenity.

*Give us each day our daily bread.*

God will provide us our needs daily as He did with the Israelites in Exodus 16.

*And forgive us our sins, for we also forgive everyone who is indebted to us.*

We are then prompted to ask for forgiveness as well as the ability to forgive others. Having the ability to openly confess your sins to God and the willingness to forgive those who have sinned against you is an imperative part of your relationship with God. Proverbs 28:9 (NIV) reads, "If anyone turns a deaf ear to my instruction, even their prayers are detestable." If the law of God requires us to confess our sins and forgive others, then we must do it. 1 John 1:8-10 says, "If we say we have no sin, we deceive ourselves, and the truth is not in us. If we confess our sins, He is faithful and just to forgive us, our sins and cleanse us from all unrighteousness. If we say that we have not sinned, we make Him a liar and His word is not in us."

*And lead us not into temptation, but deliver us from evil.*

We all encounter temptation and sometimes fall, but then we should ask God to lead us on the right path so we will not continue to walk in the ways of the evil one who comes to steal, kill, and destroy.

To be completely transparent there are moments and seasons when I'm not as committed to my prayer time as I know I should be. I used to beat myself up about it, but I realized that was exactly what the enemy wanted. So instead, I changed my mentality. When I recognize that I haven't given God as much attention as I should, I get back into reading my Bible and return to my prayer closet as if I never left. I share this because the more honest we are about our prayer lives the better off others will be. Some people may think they aren't of value if they aren't reading their Bible and praying every day, and there couldn't be anything further from the truth. There are many benefits of having time with God every day. We were created to have a relationship with Him, but please understand that God does not hold grudges if you miss spending time with Him daily. As you begin to make time for God throughout your day, it will not seem like a sacrifice and you will begin to yearn for that time with Him.

# The Victory Formation:

## Prepare for Your 21 Days of Prayer

Prayer is like a muscle that you have to exercise and commit to strengthening. For me, prayer has now become automatic. As you embark on this 21-day journey, it is essential that you have certain tools in the following sections to change, transform, or improve your prayer life.

## Read the Word of God

I make it a point not to get out of my bed without opening my Bible app and reading the Scripture of the day. Are there days when I wake up late and am in a frantic rush? Absolutely, but I don't beat myself up about it. When time permits, I open the Bible app, or open my study Bible, and read. I have come to the realization that the one thing that will always, without a doubt, be for my good is the Word of God.

If you're just starting your prayer journey, don't be ashamed or embarrassed or compare your prayer life to others. Be encouraged and know that you are not alone. Pace yourself and begin reading the Word of God in a manner that you're comfortable with. If you've never read the Bible or find it hard to understand what you've read, I recommend getting a children's storybook Bible that breaks it down in an easy digestible format. Knowing these stories will help you to understand passages of Scripture. As you mature on your prayer journey, it is important to use the Word of God in your prayers. It will help you in praying confident prayers, and it also reminds you of the promises God has made to His people. An important phrase that you can incorporate is "God, you said _____." This level of boldness demonstrates your faith in God's words. It also shows that you know that He is not a man that He shall lie, and that He will fulfill the promises He's made to His children.

By nature, I'm a reader, and I have loved reading as far back as I can remember. Most days, you'll catch me reading something on my couch. Most of the decorative accessories in my home have words on them as an extension of my love for reading. Over the years, I've changed my reading intake to be more motivational and spiritually uplifting. If you naturally don't enjoy reading, there are platforms that allow you to listen to audio recordings of the Bible.

## Fast During Your 21 Days of Prayer

In modern society, social media and television have become major distractions. Due to the lack of meaningful content, I very seldom turn on my television. Please don't get me wrong, I'm guilty of getting on social media to look for one thing and realize later that an hour has passed. To manage this, I promised myself that whatever time I spend on social media or watching television, I will spend an equal or greater amount of time with God. Whatever your guilty pleasure is, evaluate what else you could be doing with that time.

As you embark on this 21-day prayer journey fast (refrain) from social media, television, or anything else that would keep you from drawing nearer to God. Anytime you're tempted, read a passage of Scripture. If this isn't possible, or you need a slower pace, set parameters for how long you'll engage on social media or watch television, and use a timer to honor those parameters. If it's a requirement for your business or career, narrow your consumption to only be for that purpose.

## Allow God to Fill the Void

Prayer became my saving grace and I have learned to allow God to fill the void in my life. One of my challenges has been waiting on marriage. I've been single for so many years, and this made me question what might be wrong with me. I thought I had to be doing something wrong because I hadn't gotten married yet. For as long as I can remember, I wanted to be a wife. Not have a wedding, children, or this huge family, but simply become one great man's wife. As time went on and relationships turned into nightmares, that longing turned into depression, and not the depression that's antisocial, crying, and an emotional wreck, but the kind that overeats, stays busy to avoid the reality of singleness, and creates a perfect Instagram story cover-up.

I became a professional single person. I frequently took myself on date nights, which included going out to eat (at Ruth's Chris, my favorite), getting a massage, going to the movies, and closing the evening at Barnes & Noble. I basically had it down to a perfect single science. I got comfortable with the whole setup. Making it seem as if it was what I wanted masked the fact that those were all the things I wanted to be doing with my husband.

Don't get me wrong. I wasn't willing to trade my sanity and time by going on dates with someone I knew wasn't "the one", because I wasn't willing to compromise on what God promised me. I started wearing a ring with a cross as a symbol of my personal promise and commitment to God. It's a reminder that God gave a promise to give me the desires of my heart and it will not come back void. It's a reminder that He is faithful, just, and true. It's a reminder that no matter how dark it may seem or how discouraged and defeated I may feel, He hasn't forgotten about me. I have to fully trust Him and

His timing because it's way better than mine. I promised that I will keep the ring on until God directs my husband to take it off.

Had I been married when I wanted to, at the age of 23, I wouldn't be the woman I am today. I would not have grown and evolved spiritually. Through the hard times, as a single woman, I had no one to depend on but God. I know now that my future husband and his love for me are a reflection of God, but he is not God. He cannot be my all and all. I had to become one, whole, and completely dependent on God for all my needs, and my husband will have to do the same. We will be better together, in our union, because God loves us enough to make us wait until we have fully surrendered and submitted everything to Him. For all my single ladies, I'm here to tell you that God will keep His promise. Continue to pray through your singleness.

Through prayer and meditation, I've been able to hear God and understand my singleness. For you, the issue may not be marriage. It may be having a child, starting your own business, or leaving a toxic relationship. Whatever you're longing for, allow the void to be filled by God, wait on His direction and trust His timing. Know He has ordained the outcome for your good.

## God Is With You In The Game

Give yourself permission to not be perfect. There is and will only be one person to walk the face of this earth blameless and perfect. I hate to break it to you, but it is for sure Jesus and not you. Hebrews 5:9 says "and being made perfect, He became the source of eternal salvation for all those who obey Him". We all have made mistakes, done something wrong, or had thoughts that is not of God. Guess what? You are not alone! Romans 3:23 says, "For all have sinned and come short of the glory of God". There are over seven billion people on earth who are in the same battle with you. God has not called us to be perfect, but in our relationship with Him we can confess our sins, admit our faults, and look to Him to guide us in becoming better.

Stop suffering in silence, and share what you're going through. Just because you're in a storm, that doesn't mean God is not with you. In the Bible, Job lost everything in one day. His children were killed, his crops withered away, and his health instantly declined. Through it all, God was with him, and Job never cursed His name. God recognized Job's faithfulness and restored his health and gave him double for what he lost. I'm sure this did not take away the pain and sorrow Job felt, but it allowed him to have a renewed faith and the opportunity to share his new blessings with those around him.

## God's Promises

Like Job, you cannot always see the blessing in the midst of the trial. This is why He told us to walk by faith, not by sight. God does His best work when you're in trouble because that will become your testimony to remind you of His faithfulness, and to help others in similar situations. It is during these times that you have to lean and rely on Him for direction. Psalm 46 reminds us that God is a very present help in the time of trouble. Anytime God promises you something, there is a chance you will experience some type of trouble. The enemy makes it his business to make us doubt God's promise. Don't be so focused on the storm that you lose awareness of God in the storm. When you feel like you're running out of time and feel like giving up, keep pressing because you are closer to victory. When what you are pursuing happens in God's perfect timing it will happen with ease. You must trust God's timing. You may have received confirmation from God about your promise, but things still may not be working in your favor. Do not confuse this as the enemy trying to block what God has revealed. This may be a season of preparation for your promise. When God is ready to move things will happen effortlessly.

Nothing happens by mistake. God knows *all* and He is in charge. God will do things you've never seen happen before when you trust in Him. There may be times when God's promise will be seen more in what you're going through than what you hear in a sermon. Your situations and challenges will show you and others who God truly is. This is why it is so important to know the Word of God and receive direction from Him. This will serve as your foundation and a way to get confirmation from God through scriptures. Drawing nearer to God in prayer during your seasons of uncertainty will help you find peace.

## The ACTS Method of Prayer

Many people have different methods of praying. I can only tell you what has proven to work for me. I've found favor in the ACTS method. In this style of prayer, you go through the steps of Adoration, Confession, Thanksgiving, and Supplication. In addition to using this method, I include Scripture in my prayer. If you don't have any Bible verses memorized, find a few that resonate with you and commit them to memory. You strengthen your prayers by using God's words to speak over your life, over the lives of those He has called you to pray for, and over situations. His word will never come back void, and when you speak His words out loud, you increase your confidence and show God that you fully believe in Him.

**Adoration.** The first step of the ACTS method is acknowledging God for who He is. God is God alone. He doesn't need anyone or anything to be God. He is the beginning and the end. There is nothing higher or more important than Him. He is God with and without us. Psalm 48:1 (NIV) reads, "Great is the LORD, and most worthy of praise, in the city of our God, his holy mountain." Solomon gives a great example of how he gave God adoration in 2 Chronicles 6:14. "And he said: 'O LORD God of Israel, there is no God like You in the heavens or on the earth, who keeps covenants and mercy with Your servants who walk before You with all their heart.'"

**Confession.** During this second step of prayer, be very specific with your confessions. God already knows where you have fallen short and sinned, so be open and honest with Him about it. We cannot hide anything from God, so don't let more sin creep into your life by trying to hide your wrongs. We see this happen in the very beginning of time. In Genesis 3:8, Adam and Eve try to hide from God after eating the forbidden fruit. When God asks why they're hiding, He already knows. He wants to see if they will be honest and confess. As humans we sin and should be striving to be, and do better so there is no need to feel less than or ashamed.

After confessing your sins, ask God to forgive you for the sins. Feelings and actions such as fear, anxiety, jealousy, discord, gossip, lying, judgment, fornication, and adultery. The list can go on, but the point is that you have to be open and honest about how you've fallen short. Ask God to allow you to forgive yourself for these sins. Then, take it a step further and ask for forgiveness for things you may have done that you didn't even know were a sin. Last, ask God to give you a forgiving heart towards those who have sinned against you. In my prayer, I ask that God show me how to forgive those people who have knowingly or unknowingly sinned against me.

**Thanksgiving.** God has done wonderful and great things in our lives. We should spend more time thanking Him than we spend asking for more blessings. Take a moment and really think of every aspect of your day and thank God for what He's done for you. 1 Thessalonians 5:18 (NIV) reads, "give thanks in all circumstances; for this is God's will for you in Christ Jesus." A common misconception is that you should only thank God when things are going well, but you must also continue to give God thanks when you feel things aren't going well.

God has given us a promise that *all* things work together for our good (Romans 8:28) and that isn't limited to all the things you enjoy and like. When you thank God for the things that aren't going as planned in your life, it increases your faith and trust in Him. It demonstrates that you know there's a reason that "bad" situation happened to you. You trust it will be used for good, and for you to bless someone else with your testimony.

**Supplication.** In this final step of your prayer, ask God for the things you need. Bring your struggles to Him, ask for miracles to be done, get clarity, ask for confirmation, and bring the interceding requests of other people. There is nothing too big or too small to bring before God. The more you trust God with your requests, the more you will see how He has heard and answered your prayers. After you make your request, thank God once again because every request will be answered in His time and in alignment with His will. It is important to understand that God always answers our prayers, and the answer may be "no". We see this in Matthew 26 when Jesus ask God "to remove this cup" from Him. As we now know, God's answer was "no" because Jesus had to die and be resurrected for our eternal salvation.

## Get in the Zone: Experience the Benefit of a Prayer Closet or Sacred Space

Having a space dedicated for just you and God is very important. God is omnipresent, but dedicating and consecrating a space to Him strengthens your commitment to your relationship with Him. This space doesn't have to be big or fancy. Think about this. You more than likely have a space in your home dedicated for you to sleep, eat, cook, brush your teeth, shower, or "handle your business." Why would you not have a dedicated space to be with God? Matthew 6:6 reads, "But you, when you pray, enter your closet, and when you have shut your door, pray to your Father who is in secret. And your Father who sees in secret will reward you openly."

John Wesley, a theologian and driving force in the Methodist Church in the 18th century, described his mother's creative and unconventional space with God. Every day, Susanna (a wife and mother of 10) would put her apron over her head to form a tent. This was her time to spend with God, and everyone in the house knew not to bother her unless it was a dire emergency. Susanna did not have an empty closet or space in her home to set up pillows, create a prayer wall, or close the door to be with God, but she knew she had to create some type of sacred space. God will meet you in your sacred space and make it holy ground. We see this in several Scriptures throughout the Bible (Genesis 3:5, Joshua 5:15 and Acts 7:33), in which God says, "the place where you are standing is holy ground." These scriptures all symbolize God's children coming to meet and hear from Him.

Take a moment and identify a space in your home that you can dedicate as your sacred space with God. If you are having a difficult time, ask God to reveal this space to you so that you will have room to spend with Him.

## The Power of Praying Out Loud

A powerful part of prayer is praying out loud. If this is a challenge for you, start by praying out loud when you're alone. Ask God to show you how, who, and what to pray for. As you begin to pray, don't overthink your words, simply let them flow. The more you begin to pray out loud the more comfortable you will become. Often, we're afraid to say things out loud because we have a vision in our head. We don't see how it will come to pass. It's not your job to figure that out. If God has given you a vision, He will also give you a plan. Open your mouth and begin to speak life into the things God has placed on your heart and let Him take care of the rest.

For more guidance in how to pray out loud, please visit **www.JazlynDenise.com/theprayerplaybookoffer** to view a special video I created to help you master this important part of your prayer life.

> "Even so, the tongue is a little part of the body and boasts great things. See how great a forest a little fire kindles." James 3:5

## Fill the Gap: Find a Prayer Partner

A prayer partner is just as valuable as a scared space or prayer closet. I highly recommend that, prior to choosing this person, you go to God. When I entered the season of my life when I knew I needed a prayer partner in order to elevate my prayer life, I looked to God. I prayed a very specific prayer, which you will read on day 21. In doing so, I identified the person God ordained as my prayer partner.

At the time, it seemed completely insane. I knew this woman from high school, but only in passing. I didn't have a relationship with her when God revealed that she would be my prayer partner. It took me a few days to finally reach out on social media (I didn't even have her phone number), but I knew it was what God called me to do. I didn't want to make the mistake of being disobedient and miss out on my blessings. The worst thing that could happen would be that her telling me I was insane, block me on social media, and tell people I was crazy for reaching out to her. None of that happened.

I was very transparent with her about how I was praying for a prayer part-ner and God placed her on my heart. Within an hour, she responded and we scheduled a time to talk. She was in a similar spiritual place, and she was completely on board. From there, we set a schedule of when we would pray together.

On our first calls, we prayed what I call surface prayers. We didn't want to share the issues that had us in spiritual bondage. We quickly learned that for this partnership to work, we had to let our guards down. This can be extremely difficult for women because many of us have been hurt and betrayed by people close to us. The idea of telling someone your inner thoughts, struggles, issues, and insecurities is downright scary. For this reason, I can't stress enough how important it is to consult God on this decision.

As we talked more outside of our prayer calls, we developed trust and a friendship that made it easy for us to share those things we otherwise wouldn't have. Your relationship with your prayer partner will be one of the most intimate and confidential relationships you have, which is why it's so important for it to be God ordained. There has to be an extreme level of vulnerability, and it has to be a judgment-free zone. Knowing that this person will sincerely go to God in intercessory prayer on your behalf will require you to go to the next level in your faith.

Over the years, there have been times when we've been less than consistent in our scheduled prayer times, but that doesn't stop us from praying for one another in our personal time with God. When we get back in sync, it's like we haven't skipped a beat, and we're reminded of why God brought us in each other's lives. It's important that you both pray over your relationship because the enemy will not be happy about it.

Throughout the years, there have been times of spiritual warfare I wouldn't have gotten through without my prayer partner. There was a time when I was depressed and felt like I couldn't pray for myself. I talked to my prayer partner about it, and for a few weeksshe went to God on my behalf. Finally, she was very stern with me and said, "Listen. *Today* is going to be the last day we pray about this. You will not walk out of your prayer closet depressed today. Do you hear me?" I gave her a "yeah, yeah, yeah" response, and she began to pray. As I listened to her, I felt my spirit become free of all the things that had me chained. I cried out to God for myself, and we praised God together.

Although she prayed about this same issue for weeks, she had the faith that I would be healed. There's a story in the Bible (Mark 2) of four men who believed that if they could get their paralyzed friend to Jesus, he will be healed. They decided to carry him to the place where Jesus would be, but when they got there a large crowd had gathered. Their faith wouldn't let them give up so they tore off the roof and lowered the man into the room where Jesus was. Just like those men, my prayer partner knew I could be healed. Even when my faith was lacking and I didn't believe, she did.

# 21 Days of Prayer

**A**lthough I've given you prayers and Scriptures for each day, it's important for you to use them as a blueprint to write your own prayers. Your prayer life has to be specific to what you're experiencing. Use the templates in this section to begin, transform and improve your prayer life over the next 21 days.

# *Day 1*
## Prayer for Salvation

Most gracious and heavenly Father, Lord, I thank You for being good. You are great and mighty and there is no other like you. God, I come asking that You clear my heart and mind from any distractions. I ask that You forgive me for each and every one of my sins, those I have committed knowingly and unknowingly. I ask that You allow me to forgive myself and forgive those who have sinned against me. Lord, please consecrate my mind, body, and spirit to be used for You.

I come today declaring that You are the one and only true God. I ask that You enter my life, You enter my heart, and Your Holy Spirit guide my every move. I believe that You sent Your only son, Jesus, to live as a human. I believe He was born of a virgin. I believe in His miracles and His teachings. I believe He died for each and every one of my sins although He was sinless. I believe, after His crucifixion, He laid in a grave and arose on the third day with all power in His hands. I know that it is by this power that I have been saved. I have been given the right and authority to come directly to You through the Holy Spirit. I know it's because of His sacrificial blood that I have been set free from bondage and given the right to eternal life. I thank you, God, because You are so good and so gracious. Your mercy endures forever. In Jesus' name, Amen.

## The Word

And you shall love the LORD your God with all your heart and with all your soul and with all your might. Deuteronomy 6:5

For God so loved the world that He gave His only begotten Son, that whoever believes in Him should not perish, but have eternal life. John 3:16

## Power Play

Take a moment to share with God how your life has been changed and transformed through His salvation. If you've recently become saved, take this time to talk to God about how you will now use your life to help save others. Use this space to write your personal prayer of salvation.

_____

_____

_____

_____

_____

_____

_____

_____

_____

_____

_____

# *Day 2*

## Prayer to Clearly Hear the Voice of God

God, we live in a day and time when we are bombarded with noise and distractions. Give me the wisdom and strength to shut out the world and spend quality time with You. I want to hear clearly from You. Speak to me in such a way that I know it can't be anyone other than You. I am your child, and You said in Your word that Your sheep know Your voice. I thank You that no matter how big or small my problems may seem, You are always there to speak to me. I pray I am conscious to hear Your still, small voice. I know You will speak from a position of love and authority, and Your voice will align with Your word. When You speak, I want to listen and obey. In Jesus' name, Amen.

## The Word

Then He said, "Go out, and stand on the mountain before the Lord." And behold, the Lord passed by, and a great and strong wind tore into the mountains and broke the rocks in pieces before the Lord, *but* the Lord *was* not in the wind; and after the wind an earthquake, *but* the Lord *was* not in the earthquake; and after the earthquake a fire, *but* the Lord *was* not in the fire; and after the fire a still small voice. So it was, when Elijah heard *it,* that he wrapped his face in his mantle and went out and stood in the entrance of the cave. Suddenly a voice *came* to him, and said, "What are you doing here, Elijah?" 1 Kings 19:11-13 (NKJV)

He said, "If you diligently listen to the voice of the Lord your God, and do what is right in His sight, and give ear to His commandments, and keep all His statutes, I will not afflict you with any of the diseases with which I have afflicted the Egyptians. For I am the Lord who heals you." Exodus 15:26

But respond to the prayer of Your servant and to his plea, O Lord my God, to listen to the cry and prayer of Your servant who prays before You. 2 Chronicles 6:19

## Power Play

Use this space to talk to God about personal distractions that keep you from clearly hearing Him. Pray for these distractions to be removed, and talk to God about how you can better hear from Him.

_____

_____

_____

_____

_____

_____

_____

_____

_____

_____

_____

_____

_____

# *Day 3*

## Prayer of Submission

God, I come with a bowed head and humble heart. I am ready and willing to be Your servant. I submit my life to You. Use me, Lord, to build Your kingdom. I trust in Your ways and Your will, knowing that they are better than mine. Lord, give me the mind to trust You even when I don't understand. I want to do what You tell me to do when You tell me to do it. Allow me to learn the lesson You want to teach me the first time so I do not continuously encounter the same trials in my life. Use me, Lord, to minister to Your people, by allowing the light You have placed in me to shine brightly. Let the words of my mouth and the meditation of my heart be acceptable in Your sight. In Jesus' name, Amen.

## The Word

Abraham said, "My son, God will provide for Himself the lamb for a burnt offering." So the two of them went together. Genesis 22:8

Now therefore go, and I will be with your mouth and teach you what you must say. Exodus 4:12

*Power Play*

Use this space to identify ways in which you will be in submission to God. In what areas of your life have you already shown submission? In what areas are you currently struggling to submit to God?

_____

_____

_____

_____

_____

_____

_____

_____

_____

_____

_____

_____

_____

_____

_____

_____

# *Day 4*

## Prayer of Forgiveness

God, I come to You today, thanking You for giving me the ability to come directly to You and ask for forgiveness for my sins. I know we are all born into sinful nature and we live in a sinful world, but I ask that I become more like Jesus every day. Thank You for Your unconditional love, kindness, grace, mercy, and forgiveness. I thank You that when I ask to be forgiven for my past and present sins, You are a just God who grants my request. I know You don't measure my sins, and I ask that You forgive me for each one no matter how great or small I think they may be.

I ask that You show me how to forgive myself and to forgive those who have, knowingly or unknowingly, sinned against me. I don't want to hold a grudge against anyone. Right now, in the name of Jesus, I release the power to cleanse my heart by releasing all hurt, pain, rejection, neglect, and wrongdoing. I will not allow the bondage of unforgiveness to be in my spirit. I will not allow unforgiveness to be in my heart or my character. Jesus, I thank You for dying for my sins and my shortcomings. In Jesus' name, Amen.

## The Word

If My people, who are called by My name, will humble themselves and pray, and seek My face and turn from their wicked ways, then I will hear from heaven, and will forgive their sins and will heal their land. 2 Chronicles 7:14

For if you forgive men for their sins, your heavenly Father will also forgive you. But if you do not forgive men for their sins, neither will your Father forgive your sins. Matthew 6:14-15

## Power Play

Use this space to write all the things for which you need forgiveness. Be very specific.

List the people you need to forgive (even if they have never asked for forgiveness).

_____

_____

_____

_____

_____

_____

_____

_____

_____

_____

_____

# *Day 5*

## Prayer of Gratitude and Thanksgiving

My God, if I had a thousand tongues, I could not thank You enough. Your grace and mercy have carried me through. You have allowed me the opportunity to see another day among the living. I thank You for being the God who said "let there be" and there was. I thank You that when You placed the stars, sun, and moon in the sky, they never came down. I thank You for breathing life into my body and giving me the opportunity to be used by You. I thank You that all things are working together for my good. I thank You that You will never leave nor forsake me. I thank You for providing for me according to Your riches in glory. I thank You for fighting my battles. I thank You for keeping Your hand upon me and keeping evil away from me. I thank You that in spite of my sins and shortcomings, You still love me. God, I thank You for everything so I am sure to leave out nothing. In Jesus' name, Amen.

## The Word

Rejoice always. Pray without ceasing. In everything give thanks, for this is the will of God in Christ Jesus concerning you. 1 Thessalonians 5:16-18

Be anxious for nothing, but in everything by prayer and supplication with gratitude, make your request known to God. And the peace of God, which surpasses all understanding, will protect your hearts and minds through Christ Jesus. Philippians 4:6-7

## Power Play

Remember you should thank God more than you ask Him for things. The more thankful you are the more He is able to bless you because you are aware of the source of your blessings. Use this space to list the things for which you're thankful and grateful to God.

_____

_____

_____

_____

_____

_____

_____

_____

_____

_____

_____

_____

# Day 6

## Prayer for God to Show You for Whom and for What to Pray

Lord, open my heart to be receptive to clearly hear Your voice and calling. I know there are certain people and things for whom and for which You would have me to pray. It is my desire to pray for Your people in the way You desire. Allow me to pray bold prayers that move the heavens and earth, prayers that send the enemy trembling. Lord, Your people are in need, and I ask that You use me to help heal and deliver them, for the answers can only come from You. Our nation is in turmoil, and only You can bring peace. Use me, Lord. I am Your servant, and it is my will for Your will to be done. In Jesus' name, Amen.

## The Word

Create in me a clean heart, O God, and renew a right spirit within me. Psalm 51:10

A man's heart devises his way, but the LORD directs his steps. Proverbs 16:9

*Power Play*

Use this space to write the names and situations God has placed in your mind and on your heart. These people and things don't come to mind by coincidence. You may not have details about what they need prayer for, but ask God to give you direction in praying for them.

_____

_____

_____

_____

_____

_____

_____

_____

_____

_____

_____

_____

_____

_____

## Day 1

# Prayer for the Courage and Strength to Pray for God's People

Father God, I come before You today asking that You give me the courage and strength to pray for Your people. I understand this is not a task to be taken lightly. I know You have fully equipped me to be a prayer warrior for You. I am ready to go to battle with the enemy to enlarge Your kingdom and recruit soldiers for Your army. May the words of my mouth and the meditation of my heart be acceptable in Your sight, Lord. In Jesus' name, Amen.

## The Word

Brothers, if any one of you strays from the truth and someone corrects him, let him know that he who converts the sinner from the error of his way will save a soul from death and will cover a multitude of sins. James 5:19-20

Power Play

Use this space to talk to God about your personal weaknesses in praying for yourself and His people. What do you need to develop a stronger ability to pray for God's people?

_____

_____

_____

_____

_____

_____

_____

_____

_____

_____

_____

_____

_____

# Day 8

## Prayer for Wisdom

Lord, it is my prayer that daily You endow me with Your wisdom. Allow the same wisdom given to Solomon to be the ministry of my life. Let me not think or move with haste, but in a timely manner after allowing You to speak. God, Your wisdom will keep me out of trouble. Your wisdom will allow me to make the right decisions. Your wisdom will give me the words to say to Your people. Your wisdom will open doors and humble hearts. Your word says You generously give wisdom to those who ask, so Lord I come to You believing in Your word. Allow my wisdom to help others in their time of need. In Jesus'. name, Amen.

## The Word

"Now give wisdom and knowledge to me so that I might know how to go before this people, for who can judge this great people of Yours?" Then God responded to Solomon, "Because this was in your heart and you did not ask for possessions, wealth, and honor, or even the life of those who hate you, nor have you asked for many days of life, but you have asked Me for wisdom and knowledge that you might govern My people over whom I have made you king, wisdom and knowledge are now given to you. Possessions, wealth, and honor I will also give to you; such has not been given to kings before you nor those who will follow after you." 2 Chronicles 1:10-12

If any of you lacks wisdom, let him ask of God who gives to all men liberally and without criticism, and it will be given to him. James 1:5

## Power Play

Use this space to talk to God about areas of your life where you lack wisdom and thank Him for the areas where your wisdom is evident.

_____

_____

_____

_____

_____

_____

_____

_____

_____

_____

_____

# *Day 9*

# Prayer for God-Directed Decisions

Lord, it is my desire to be in total alignment with Your will for my life. I want You to be the head of all that I do. I know I will make mistakes if I do not trust in Your direction. Lord, allow me the faith to trust in You even when I don't understand. Give me the faith and hope to know that You and Your word cannot and will not fail. God, I thank you that no decision is too big or small for you to answer. It is my desire to look to You for answers in all things so my life will follow in the path You have prepared for me. Order my steps, Lord. Guide my feet in Your Word. In Jesus's name, Amen.

## The Word

Teach me good discernment and knowledge, for I have believed Your commandments. Psalm 119:66

Trust in the LORD with all your heart, and lean not on your own understanding; in all your ways acknowledge Him, and He will direct your paths. Proverbs 3:5-6

## Power Play

Use this space to talk to God about decisions you are currently in the process of making. What have you heard God tell you about these decisions?

_____

_____

_____

_____

_____

_____

_____

_____

_____

_____

_____

# *Day 10* ↘

## Prayer for Your Family and Loved Ones

Lord, You knew me before I was formed in my mother's womb. Therefore, You knew the family into which I would be born. Continue to strengthen us and bind us closer each day. If there is any strife among us, I cast it back to the pits of hell in the name of Jesus. Give me the heart of Joseph to understand that even when my family may not treat me right, You are using it for my good. Allow us to speak to one another in love. Let us encourage one another. Break generational curses and breathe a fresh anointing.

Lord, show us how to minister to one another and uplift each other. Let us be stepping stones for one another and not stumbling blocks. Strengthen my relationship with each member of my family. Lord, I know You also have placed special people in my life. We may not share the same DNA, but You have ushered them into my life to serve as part of my family. I pray that You continue to cover and nurture those relationships as well. In Jesus' name, Amen.

## The Word

I will turn toward you and make you fruitful and multiply you, and I will confirm My covenant with you. Leviticus 26:9

Train up a child in the way he should go, and when he is old he will not depart from it. Proverbs 22:6

Love suffers long and is kind; love envies not; love flaunts not itself and is not puffed up, does not behave itself improperly, seeks not its own, is not easily provoked, thinks no evil; rejoices not in iniquity, but rejoices in the truth; bears all things, believes all things, hopes all things, and endures all things. 1 Corinthians 13:4-7

Power Play

Use this space to thank God for your family and loved ones. List them by name and thank God for them.

If you have an issue with a particular person, write it out and use the word of God to guide you in how to mend things, cope with the situation, or set boundaries with that person.

_____

_____

_____

_____

_____

_____

_____

_____

_____

_____

# *Day 11*

## Prayer for Your Business and/or Career

ather God, my works are committed to You. I don't take for granted the gifts and talents You've given me. I ask that You continue to give me the vision to be diligent about the work You have for me to do during my time here on earth. Bestow Your favor upon me while giving me and guidance Lord, as I work, allow me to do so as if I am personally working for You. Place the right people in my path to assist in enlarging my territory. God, allow my name and my business to be positively spoken about in the rooms where decisions are made, in meetings where generational wealth is created, and at the time you have set for me to thrive.

Your word says that my gift will open doors for me, and I know these are doors only You can open. You don't always call the qualified, but You always qualify the called. I pray for a supernatural covering and a special anointing over my career and my business. As my responsibilities continue to grow, I pray that You provide me with the means to create a healthy work-life balance. Lord, in striving for excellence I don't want to experience burnout but rather enjoy the fruits of my labor. In Jesus' name, Amen.

## *The Word*

Then Jabez called on the God of Israel, saying "Oh, that You would indeed bless me and enlarge my territory, that Your hand might be with me, and that You would keep me from evil, that it may not bring me hardship!" So God granted what he asked. 1 Chronicles 4:10

Commit your works to the LORD, and your thoughts will be established. Proverbs 16:3

For when we were with you, we commanded you that if any will not work, neither shall he eat. 2 Thessalonians 3:10

Power Play

Use this space to write out the visions God has given you. What are you passionate about? What would you do even if there was no financial compensation? Who or what do you need to help you successfully bring your visions to life?

_____

_____

_____

_____

_____

_____

_____

_____

_____

_____

_____

_____

_____

# *Day 12*

## Prayer Over Your Finances

Lord, I thank You for being a provider. There have been times when I had more bills than money, but You remained faithful and just. I ask that You continue to show me favor in regards to my money. Lord, I thank You for every penny You have blessed me with. Show me how to be a good steward over my money. Lord, as I receive money, I want to commit it to You first by being a cheerful giver through my tithes and offering. Forgive me for the times when I have not trusted in You to provide all of my needs with the finances you have made me a steward over. Lord, I fully trust You with my finances and know You are able to provide abundantly and exceedingly more than I could ever imagine. I pray that I look to You in creating a manageable budget that affords me to save and invest. I pray that in being wise with my finances, I will be the creator of generational wealth in my family. I trust in You, Lord. I know You can and You will be my ultimate provider, and I thank You for Your provisions. In Jesus' name, Amen.

## The Word

Jacob vowed a vow saying, "If God will be with me and will protect me in this way that I go, and will give me bread to eat and clothing to put on, so that I return to my father's house in peace, then the LORD will be my God. Then this stone, which I have set for a pillar, will be the house of God, and from all that You give me I will surely give a tenth to You." Genesis 28:20-22

But you must remember the LORD your God, for it is He who gives you the ability to get wealth, so that He may establish His covenant which He swore to your fathers, as it is today. Deuteronomy 8:18

A feast is made for laughter, wine makes life merry, and money is the answer for everything. Ecclesiastes 10:19 (NIV)

Honor the LORD with your substance, and with the first fruits of all your increase; so your barns will be filled with plenty and your presses will burst out with new wine. Proverbs 3:9-10

But my God shall supply your needs according to His riches in glory in Christ Jesus. Philippians 4:19

Will a man rob God? Yet you have robbed Me. But you say, "How have we robbed You?" In tithes and offering. You are cursed with a curse, your whole nation, for you are robbing Me. Bring all the tithes into the storehouse, that there may be food in My house, and test Me now in this, says the LORD of Hosts, if I will not open for you the windows of heaven and pour out for you a blessing, that there will not be room enough to receive it. Malachi 3:8-10

*Power Play*

Use this space to thank God and pray over every penny He has given you.

Talk to God about the struggles you have with being a good steward over your money.

What financial goals do you have, and what do you plan to do in the kingdom of God once you've reached that goal?

_____

_____

_____

_____

_____

_____

_____

# *Day 13* ↘
## Prayer for God's Promises

Lord, I thank You that You have promised to never leave or forsake me. I thank You that, even when I am in the midst of trials and tribulations, I can trust that *all* things are working together for my good. I know in this promise You will even use things that the enemy meant to harm me for my good. I thank You that You will never place more on me than I can handle. I thank You for being the God that keeps His promises. You are the great "I AM," and I trust and believe in Your Word. I know that Your promises cannot return void. I know You hear each and every one of my prayers, and even when I don't like the answer I have to trust it is Your will for my life.

God, continue to show me Your promises every day so I can share the good and great news of how faithful You are. I want the promises You have given me to be a blessing to others. I want Your promises to help me lead someone to a deeper and stronger relationship with You. I believe in Your promises, I trust in Your promises, and I am so grateful for Your promises. In Jesus' name, Amen.

## The Word

Abraham called the name of that place The LORD Will Provide, as it is said to this day, "In the mount of the LORD it will be provided." Genesis 22:14

Be strong and of a good courage. Fear not, nor be afraid of them, for the LORD your God, it is He who goes with you. He will not fail you, nor forsake you." Deuteronomy 31:6

## Power Play

Use this space to write the specific promises (a relationship, a child, financial peace, physical or emotional healing, etc.) you are expecting God to bring forth in your life. Also, identify scriptures that relate to your promise.

_____

_____

_____

_____

_____

_____

_____

_____

_____

_____

_____

_____

_____

_____

_____

_____

_____

*Day 14*  ↘

# Prayer for Your Future or Current Husband/Wife

## Woman's Prayer for Your Future Husband:

God, my Father, my Healer, my Comforter, my Creator, I come to You, Lord, humbly knowing that You hold my heart in Your hands. You know my needs, desires, and wants, Lord. As I bow to You at Your throne of grace, I ask that You cleanse me and wash me with the blood of Jesus. Give me the strength and power to move forward as only You can, Lord. I thank You for being a God who has heard my cry. I thank You for being a God who allowed me to learn the lessons of heartache so I can appreciate the man of God You have created for me. Thank You for allowing me to be alone, so I can get closer to You and become a better wife for him.

I don't take for granted any day, hour, minute, or second. I know that my time as a single woman is for my good. Lord, thank You for giving me patience to wait on You. Thank You for giving me wisdom to wait on You, and thank You for giving me perseverance to continue to have faith in You. I know You are not a man that you should lie and Your word can never come back void. I thank You for loving me enough to have created my husband just for me, in Your image and likeness. I will continue to trust and believe in You, oh God, my Strength and my Redeemer. In Jesus' name, Amen.

## Woman's Prayer for Your Husband:

Most gracious and heavenly Father, I come to you today thanking you for my husband. I am grateful that You loved me so much that You created him. Continue to use us and our marriage as a ministry for others. Give my husband the wisdom and knowledge to know he must submit himself to You and lead our family. I pray he continues to strive to live a life of purpose and continues to be faithful to You. I pray we remain patient with one another. Our marriage is not and will not be perfect, but I know we are able to endure anything with You as our foundation.

Show us how to pray for one another and uplift each other through our words and actions. I pray we keep our priorities in alignment with You. I thank you that my husband is a man of valor and integrity. I thank you that he seeks you first and the outpouring of love You give him overflows in our relationship. Allow us to speak with honesty, openness, and transparency so we do not allow the enemy to enter into our relationship. Cover us with the blood of Jesus.

Your Word says we are to be financially sound and equally yoked. I pray we remain physically attracted to one another and do not yield to any sexual temptations outside of our marriage. Bind our spirits together and allow us to walk in forgiveness for any past wrongdoings. This is a new day You have given us, and the fruit of the Spirit will dwell in our home. In the mighty name of Jesus, Amen.

## Man's Prayer for Your Future Wife:

God, my Father, my Healer, my Comforter, my Creator, I come to You, Lord, humbly knowing that You hold my heart in Your hands. You know my needs, desires, and wants, Lord. As I bow to You at Your throne of grace, I ask that You cleanse me and wash me with the blood of Jesus. Give me the strength and power to move forward as only You can, Lord. I thank You for being a God who has heard my cry. I thank You for being a God who allowed me to learn the lessons of heartache so I can appreciate the woman of God You have created for me. Thank You for allowing me to be alone, so I can get closer to You and become a better husband for her.

I don't take for granted any day, hour, minute, or second. I know that my time as a single man is for my good. Lord, thank You for giving me patience to wait on You. Thank You for giving me wisdom to wait on You, and thank You for giving me perseverance to continue to have faith in You. I know that You are not a man that you should lie and Your word can never come back void. I thank You for loving me enough to have created my wife just for me, in Your image and likeness. I will continue to trust and believe in You, oh God, my Strength and my Redeemer. In Jesus' name, Amen.

## Man's Prayer for Your Wife:

Most gracious and heavenly Father, I come to you today thanking you for my wife. I am grateful that You loved me so much that You created her. Continue to use us and our marriage as a ministry for others. Give my wife the wisdom and knowledge to know she must submit herself to You and follow my lead for our family. I pray she continues to strive to live a life of purpose and continues to be faithful to You. I pray we remain patient with one another. Our marriage is not and will not be perfect, but I know we are able to endure anything with You as our foundation.

Show us how to pray for one another and uplift each other through our words and actions. I pray we keep our priorities in alignment with You. I thank you that my wife is a woman of integrity. I thank you that she seeks you first and the outpouring of love You give her overflows in our relationship. Allow us to speak with honesty, openness, and transparency so we do not allow the enemy to enter into our relationship. Cover us with the blood of Jesus.

Your Word says we are to be financially sound and equally yoked. I pray we remain physically attracted to one another and do not yield to any sexual temptations outside of our marriage. Bind our spirits together and allow us to walk in forgiveness for any past wrongdoings. This is a new day You have given us, and the fruit of the Spirit will dwell in our home. In the mighty name of Jesus, Amen.

# The Word

Then the LORD God said, "It is not good that the man should be alone, I will make a helper suitable for him." Genesis 2:18

Every wise woman builds her house, but the foolish pulls it down with her hands. Proverbs 14:1

Whoever finds a wife finds a good thing, and obtains favor of the LORD. Proverbs 18:22

Two are better than one, because there is a good reward for their labor together. For if they fall, then one will help up his companion. But woe to him who is alone when he falls and has no one to help him up. Also if two lie down together, then they will keep warm; but how can one keep warm by himself? And if someone might overpower another by himself, two together can withstand him. A threefold cord is not quickly broken. Ecclesiastes 4:9-12

## Power Play

(Single women/men) Use this space to write every detail about what you need in your husband/wife.

What do you personally need to improve to be whole before God brings this person into your life?

What steps and tools are you using to prepare?

_____

_____

_____

_____

_____

_____

_____

**Power Play** ✗

(Married women/men) Use this space to write a message to your husband/wife. Thank him specifically for being the man/woman God created for you.

Write out all the things you need forgiveness for in your marriage and all the things for which you forgive your husband/wife.

Finally, write what you want God to do in your marriage to make it more of a ministry for His kingdom.

_____

_____

_____

_____

_____

_____

_____

_____

# *Day 15* ↘
## Prayer to Resist Temptation

Lord, I know I will be tempted by the enemy, but You are much stronger than him. Just as Jesus asked that You lead us not into temptation, I ask the same of You on this day. Lord, show me the things I am tempted by so I can acknowledge them by name. Give me the strength to be aware of my temptations and resist them. Your word says if I submit myself to You, and resist the devil, he must flee from me. I come completely submitting to You so Your hand can remain upon me. I want to pass the test when I am tempted and know I can only do that by the strength You have placed in me. Allow that strength to increase daily. In Jesus' name, Amen.

## The Word

No temptation has taken you except what is common to man. God is faithful, and He will not permit you to be tempted above what you can endure, but will with the temptation also make a way to escape, that you may be able to bear it. 1 Corinthians 10:13

My brothers, count it all joy when you fall into diverse temptations, knowing that the trying of your faith develops patience. But let patience perfect its work, that you may be perfect and complete, lacking nothing. James 1:2-4

Submit yourselves, then, to God. Resist the devil, and he will flee from you. James 4:7 (NIV)

## Power Play

Use this space to list the things that bring temptation into your life.

What can you do to defeat the enemy when he brings this temptation to you?

What specific scriptures speak to your temptation?

_____

_____

_____

_____

_____

_____

_____

_____

_____

_____

# Day 16

## Prayer to Get Through Trials and Tribulations

Father God, just as you were with Shadrach, Meshach, and Abednego in the fire, I ask that You be with me. I know I will be tempted and endure trials, but I also know You will be there with me in the midst of it all. Just as You were with Daniel in the lion's den be with me. When he was lifted out of the den untouched it made the king, and his nation believe in You, because You gave him victory. God, You provided a stone for David to slay Goliath when no one else could. In all of these trials and tribulations, it seemed as if there was no way to win, but You have countless stories of defeating the odds and coming out victorious. I know if I come up against a trial, You will be there with me to guide me through. I ask that I trust in You, Your word, and Your promises. In Jesus' name, Amen.

## The Word

Blessed is the man who endures temptation, for when he is tried, he will receive the crown of life, which the Lord has promised to those who love Him. James 1:12

I do not speak because I have need, for I have learned in whatever state I am to be content. I know both how to face humble circumstances and how to have abundance. Everywhere and in all things I have learned the secret, both to be full and to be hungry, both to abound and to suffer need. Philippians 4:11-12

## Power Play

Use this space to write about your current challenges. In what way do you need God to guide you through this storm?

If you don't currently have any challenges, reflect on past trials and tribulations and find ways to turn them into a testimony to help someone.

_____

_____

_____

_____

_____

_____

_____

_____

_____

# Day 17

## Prayer to Let the Enemy Know
## He Is Already Defeated

Father God, I thank You for not just fighting my battles, but for being victorious in them. In James 4:7, Your word says "Therefore submit yourselves to God. Resist the devil, and he will flee from you." Right now, in the name of Jesus, I put the enemy (Satan/the devil/Lucifer) on high alert, knowing I am saved and covered by the blood of Jesus.

I send you back to the pits of hell where you belong, Satan. You are not welcome to any part of my life. You have no power or authority. You are a liar, deceptive and evil. There is nothing you have that I want. As the Word of God says, I have swept my house clean of you and your demons. The word says you will return with more powerful spirits, but know that the angels of my good and gracious God are surrounding me, my home, my finances, my relationships, my family, my friends, my business/career/schooling, my mind, my heart, my spirit, my body, and every single thing I touch.

God, You have given me authority over the enemy, and I declare and decree he has and will continue to be defeated by the blood of Jesus. God, thank You for keeping Your hand upon me and keeping the enemy far from me. Thank You for being with me during every attack, for Your Word says You will never leave or forsake me. Thank You for fighting. In Jesus' name, Amen.

## The Word

The LORD your God who goes before you, He shall fight for you, just as all that He did for you in Egypt before your eyes, and in the wilderness, where you saw how the LORD your God carried you, as a man carries his son, in all the way that you went, until you came to this place. Deuteronomy 1:30-31

Then Jesus said to him, "Get away from here Satan! For it is written, 'You shall worship the Lord your God, and Him only shall you serve.'" Then the devil left Him, and immediately angels came and ministered to Him. Matthew 4:10-11

Finally, my brothers, be strong in the Lord and in the power of His might. Put on the whole armor of God that you may be able to stand against the schemes of the devil. For our fight is not against flesh and blood, but against principalities, against powers, against the rulers of the darkness of this world, and against spiritual forces of evil in the heavenly places. Therefore take up the whole armor of God that you may be able to resist in the evil day, and having done all, to stand. Stand therefore, having your waist girded with the truth, having put on the breastplate of righteousness, having your feet fitted with the readiness of the gospel of peace, and above all, taking the shield of faith, with which you will be able to extinguish all the fiery arrows of the evil one. Take the helmet of salvation and the sword of the Spirit, which is the word of God. Pray in the Spirit always with all kinds of prayer and supplication. To that end be alert with all perseverance and supplication for all the saints. Ephesians 6:10-18

He said to them, "I saw Satan as lightning fall from heaven. Look, I give you authority to trample on serpents and scorpions, and over all the power of the enemy. And nothing shall by any means hurt you. Nevertheless do not rejoice that the spirits are subject to you, but rather rejoice that your names are written in heaven. Luke 10:18-20

Power Play

Use this space to speak directly to the enemy. Tell him how he has already been defeated in your life. Use the word of God to show the enemy your authority over him and list the things in your life over which he has no control.

---
---
---
---
---
---

# *Day 18* ⤷
## Prayer to Walk Fully in Your Blessings

God, I can never thank You enough for all the things You have blessed me with. Lord, daily You show me Your wondrous works. God, I know if I continue to trust and believe in the path You have set before me, You will lead me to more blessings. I fully acknowledge these blessings are for me to bless Your people and to show others how faithful You are. Lord, there is nothing that will be withheld from me as long as I remain faithful to You. Doors I knock on will be answered, and as I seek I will find.

Set me on high so I can see the things You have on the horizon. Elevate my thinking and make my path straight. Put the right people around me to help strengthen my gifts. As I walk in my blessings, keep me humble, but not ashamed of what You have done for me. I don't want to hide my blessing because of someone else's insecurities. I know there will be people who are not happy with the way You have blessed me, and I ask that You remove those individuals from my life. Let me be surrounded by positivity, encouragement, and love. In Jesus' name, Amen.

## The Word

But the manifestation of the Spirit is given to everyone for the common good. To one is given by the Spirit the word of wisdom, to another the word of knowledge by the same Spirit, to another faith by the same Spirit, to another gifts of healings by the same Spirit, to another the working of miracles, to another prophecy, to another discerning of spirits, to another various kinds of tongues, and to another the interpretation of tongues. But that one and very same Spirit works all these, dividing to each one individually as He will. 1 Corinthians 12: 7-11

I can do all things because of Christ who strengthens me. Philippians 4:13

Power Play

Use this space to list your blessings. Name the moments in your life when you have seen God's favor.

_____

_____

_____

_____

_____

_____

_____

_____

_____

_____

_____

_____

_____

_____

# Day 19

## Prayer to Fill You with the Holy Spirit

Lord, I believe Jesus was raised from the dead with all power in His hands. I believe what He said when He told the disciples You would send a Helper and they would be filled with the Holy Spirit. Your Word says You will give the Holy Spirit to those who ask so I come, Lord, asking be filled until I overflow. I know that same Spirit dwells in me and I have the ability to utilize it. Lord, I know being filled with the Holy Spirit is a gift, and I don't ever want to take it for granted. Let every moment in the Spirit be sacred. Allow me to live in the moment and be present with You. In Jesus' name, Amen.

## The Word

But the Helper, the Holy Spirit, whom the Father will send in My name, He will teach you all things, and bring to your remembrance all things that I said to you. John 14:26 (NKJV)

After they prayed, the place where they were meeting was shaken. And they were all filled with the Holy Spirit and spoke the word of God boldly. Acts 4:31 (NIV)

Power Play

Write about ways you have experienced God's Holy Spirit.

Use this space to invite the Holy Spirit into your life.

_____

_____

_____

_____

_____

_____

_____

_____

_____

_____

_____

_____

# *Day 20* ↴

## Prayer to Walk by Faith and Continue Believing

Father God, it is my desire to completely trust in You and Your Word. Lord, having faith and belief requires me to have the courage I need to trust Your Word. I ask, today, that You increase my faith. Show me how to recall the things You've done, and help me to remember that if You before did it You will do it again. I have put my faith in trivial things, like pressing on the brakes of my car and believing they will work. When I get on a plane I have faith that the pilot has been trained and knows how to safely land the plane. If I can have faith in man and man-made objects, I should, without a doubt, have much more faith in You.

You are the Creator of all things. You are the God who said "Let there be" and it was so. You are the God who placed the sun and moon in the sky, and they have never come down. Lord, my faith doesn't waiver because I fail to believe You are able to do what You said you would do, but rather it waivers because I don't always think I am able or worthy. Strengthen me today so my faith increases, and allow me to acknowledge that only You can make the unseen come to fruition. In Jesus' name, Amen.

## *The Word*

Immediately the father of the child cried out with tears, "Lord, I believe. Help my unbelief!" Mark 9:24

So faith by itself, if it has no works, is dead. James 2:17

But let him ask in faith, without wavering. For he who wavers is like a wave of the sea, driven and tossed with the wind. Let not that man think that he will receive anything from the Lord. A double-minded man is unstable in all his ways. James 1:6-8

Now faith is the substance of things hoped for, the evidence of things not seen. Hebrews 11:1

*Power Play*

Use this space to reflect on times when you've walked by faith and not by sight. What were the outcomes?

Write about areas of your life where your faith is weak and ask God to strengthen you in these specific areas.

_____

_____

_____

_____

_____

_____

_____

_____

_____

_____

_____

_____

_____

# Day 21

## Prayer to Identify a Prayer Partner

Heavenly Father, I come to You with a bowed head and humble heart. God, I ask that You clear my mind, body and spirit of anything that is not of You. Forgive me of my sins. [Say them out loud as they come to your mind.] Consecrate my heart and mind so I may clearly hear Your voice. I thank You for giving me a spirit of discernment. I thank You for allowing me to effectively use my intuition. I thank You for knowing my needs and providing them even when I don't ask or deserve it.

I come to You asking that You give me guidance and direction in partnering with someone in prayer. Allow my prayer partner to walk in the Fruit of the Spirit (love, joy, peace, patience, kindness, goodness, faithfulness, gentleness, and self-control). Your Word says that where two or three are gath-ered, You will be in the midst of them. I pray that this person be faithful to You and together we will be able to bring down strongholds, for You said "One would put a thousand to flight and two would put ten thousand to flight."

God, I am ready to excel in my prayer life. Give me the wisdom I need to move forward with this decision. I have full faith and trust in You. For You are a God who cannot fail. Guide me in identifying this person, and when it is clear, give me the right timing and the words to say. Take away any fear or anxiety I may have about this process, and cover me as I obey You. I thank You in advance that the partnership You have ordained will be a blessing not just to us but to others. Keep Your hand upon us and keep evil far from us. In Jesus' name, Amen.

## The Word

How should one chase a thousand, and two put ten thousand to flight, unless their Rock had sold them, and the LORD had given them up? Deuteronomy 32:30

Behold how good and how pleasant it is for brother to dwell together in unity! Psalm 133:1

Confess your faults to one another and pray for one another, that you may be healed. The effective fervent prayer of the righteous man accomplishes much. James 5:16

Power Play

Use this space to identify the characteristics you need in a prayer partner.

In what ways will you enrich this person's life?

What boundaries do you need to overcome to allow this relationship to flourish?

_____

_____

_____

_____

_____

_____

_____

_____

_____

_____

# You did it!

In 21 days, you have changed, transformed, and improved your prayer life. Take a moment to reflect on what you've experienced over the last three weeks.

Now that you're on a roll, don't stop. Remember, if you fall off, it isn't hard to start back where you were. I'm extremely proud of you, and I'm grateful to have been part of your prayer journey.

May God continue to keep and bless you.

# About the Author

Jazlyn Denise

Our Generation's Prayer Partner, Jazlyn Denise, is bringing to life her vision for millions of people to have a more intimate relationship with God through prayer. A preacher's kid, who grew up in the church founded by her maternal grandparents, Jazlyn was surprised to realize she'd never learned to pray in a way that felt fully authentic. In just a few weeks, she turned around her prayer life, and in doing so, found her calling. As a motivational speaker, workshop leader, and prayer coach, Jazlyn teaches believers to pray with confidence and ease.